I'm Not Sleepy!

Colin and Jacqui Hawkins

WALKER BOOKS
LONDON

Time for bed, Baby Bear.

THIS WALKER BOOK BELONGS TO:

_____

_____

_____

_____

First published 1985 by
Walker Books Ltd
87 Vauxhall Walk
London SE11 5HJ

This edition published 1993

©1985 Colin and Jacqui Hawkins

Printed and bound in Hong Kong by
South China Printing Co. (1988) Ltd

British Library Cataloguing in Publication Data
A catalogue record for this book is
available from the British Library.

ISBN 0-7445-3042-3

Sweet dreams, Baby Bear.

MORE WALKER PAPERBACKS
For You to Enjoy

Also by Colin & Jacqui Hawkins

FARMYARD SOUNDS / JUNGLE SOUNDS

"Lots of jolly cartoon-style animals… Every child I've ever
known loves making animal noises, so be prepared
to do your stuff." *Tony Bradman, Parents*

Farmyard Sounds   0-7445-1752-4
Jungle Sounds   0-7445-1753-2
£3.99 each

TERRIBLE TERRIBLE TIGER / THE WIZARD'S CAT

Two wonderfully entertaining rhyming picture books
about a tiger who is not quite what he seems
and a cat who wishes he were something else!

Terrible Terrible Tiger   0-7445-1063-5   £3.99
The Wizard's Cat   0-7445-1389-8   £2.99

WHERE'S MY MUMMY?

Duckling is looking for his mummy. But who is it?
Is it the dog, the cat or the hen? Where is his mummy?
Young children will have great fun helping duckling
to bring his search to a happy conclusion.

0-7445-3041-5   £3.99

**Walker Paperbacks are available from most booksellers, or by post from
Walker Books Ltd, PO Box 11, Falmouth, Cornwall TR10 9EN.**

To order, send: Title, author, ISBN number and price for each book ordered, your full name and address, cheque or postal order
for the total amount, plus postage and packing: UK and BFPO Customers – £1.00 for first book, plus 50p for the second book
and plus 30p for each additional book to a maximum charge of £3.00. Overseas and Eire Customers – £2.00 for first book,
plus £1.00 for the second book and plus 50p per copy for each additional book.
Prices are correct at time of going to press, but are subject to change without notice.